The Christmas Story

The Christmas Story

as Told by Edgar Cayce

Compiled and edited by
Jon Robertson

Illustrated by Glenna Hartwell

A·R·E
PRESS

ASSOCIATION FOR
RESEARCH AND
ENLIGHTENMENT

A.R.E. Press • Virginia Beach • Virginia

A.R.E. Press
Sixty-Eighth & Atlantic Avenue
P.O. Box 656
Virginia Beach, VA 23451-0656

Library of Congress Cataloging-in-Publication Data
   Cayce, Edgar, 1877-1945.
   The Christmas story : as told by Edgar Cayce / compiled and edited by Jon Robertson : illustrated by Glenna Hartwell.
       p.   cm.
   ISBN 0-87604-356-2
   1. Jesus Christ—Nativity—Miscellanea. 2. Jesus Christ—Spiritualistic interpretations. I. Robertson, Jon. II. Title.
BT315.2.C39   1996
232.92–dc20
                                              96-31155

Cover design by John Comerford and Kim Cohen

Contents

Illustrations

About the Book

THE MARVELOUS EVENTS that took place on the first Christmas are known throughout the world, but this book tells the story from an extraordinary point of view. On these pages, you will read the familiar narrative of the birth of Jesus, with the added insights found in the psychic readings of Edgar Cayce, the most well-documented clairvoyant of our time.

People who are familiar with Cayce's work know that the highly accurate psychic information contained in his readings came from spiritual sources, while he lay in an apparently hypnotic state. Even though Cayce often gave readings to people who were not in his presence, those who requested readings would usually sit by his side while their questions were asked. The questions asked of Cayce, during the over 14,000 readings that he gave in his lifetime, yielded answers that cover nearly every subject. The readings were all written down by a stenographer and are available today at the Association for Research and Enlightenment, Inc. (A.R.E.), in Virginia

Beach, Virginia, to anyone who wishes to study them.

The special details found in the readings, which were given during the first half of this century, answer many of the questions that are simply not provided in the gospels. The Cayce readings reveal previously unknown information about Mary and Joseph, the Immaculate Conception, Jesus' birth in Bethlehem, and the family's sojourn in Egypt.

In narrative form, this book provides these missing insights. It also includes the story of how Mary was visited by the angel and information about Mary's mother, Anna. You will also enjoy reading about Mary's early life of training among the Essene religious sect, which had prepared for many years for the coming of the Messiah by training and teaching young students like her.

Readers will enjoy learning about some of the people who participated in Mary's preparation for conceiving and giving birth to Jesus. There was Judy, the Essene teacher and scribe, who not only taught Mary, but later taught Jesus as well. There was also Apsaphar, the innkeeper, and Josie, who accompanied the Holy Family to Egypt after Herod's terrible edict.

In the Cayce readings, the Christmas story is not told all in one place or in one reading. Instead, the individual bits of information are scattered throughout the readings collection and have been researched, brought together, and edited in order to make the story easy to read.

This little book of *The Christmas Story* has had a colorful history, and a number of researchers have contributed to it.

In 1956, author Mary Ellen Carter created a booklet entitled *The Christmas Story,* edited by Margaret Gammon, that presented portions of several pertinent readings in a logical sequence. A booklet entitled *A Story of Jesus,* compiled by Clifford P. Owens and first published in 1963, has also been used. Other research came from a booklet entitled *Edgar Cayce's Story of Christmas* by L. M. Selover, originally published by the A.R.E. Youth Activities Department in 1987. The present work contains elements of these booklets, the biblical account of Luke, and additional research and writing provided in 1996 by A.R.E. Press editor, Jon Robertson.

In an effort to remain truthful to the spirit of the Cayce readings, the story in this book is told in language kept as close as possible to the language used by Cayce when he gave the readings.

During Cayce's lifetime, each person or group who received a reading was identified by a number. For example, reading number 1472-2 indicates that this was the second reading received by the person identified as 1472. A complete list of readings used in the book appears at the back.

This book, illustrated by nationally known artist Glenna Hartwell, has been created for the entire family to enjoy, whether you wish to read it in private or aloud at group gatherings.

As you read this narrative, remember that it is neither a legend, nor a fairy tale, nor a work of fiction—but information that has come from a highly dependable spiritual source. Let the facts wash over you, and let your mind be guided to see the truth of the wondrous birth of Jesus the

Christ, the way it really was.

The editors and staff of A.R.E. hope that this book will help all readers find within their hearts the living spirit of the Christmas story and that it will bring them joy throughout the year.

A Psalm for Christmas

Come! Let us make a joyous noise unto the Lord,
The rock of our salvation,
Who in times past and in the present
Makes known the joyous message unto
The sons and daughters of humankind:

For there is alive this day
The Christ spirit that came
As upon the wings of the angels,
That made known the glad tidings
Unto the men and women in that far land.

He is not far away today!
But in our own hearts may we
Hear that voice come to us and say,
"Peace! Be still! It is I, fear not,
For I, thy Savior, am with thee this day."

(281-14)

The Christmas Spirit Within

s you approach the Season that means so much to every student of Christian thought, may you know what the birth of the Christ-Child in Jesus has meant. May you know that it does mean more in the thought and activity of the world as a whole. And you may judge within yourselves as to whether the world is growing better or not, according to the manifestation of the Christ-mass or Christmas spirit in thy daily life and thy associations with thy fellow human beings.

For unless this fact is a personal experience, then to you, as an individual, it is not being accomplished.

But you can feel the peace within, as it comes from meditating upon the desire to be what the Father-God would have you be through the promises in the Christ-Jesus when your life, your associations with your fellow men and women are made more and more in keeping with the Christmas spirit; which is the manifestation of the commandment He gave, "A new commandment give

I unto you, that ye love one another, even as I have loved you."

Let that love, that beauty, which was the message to the shepherds, be yours today: "Unto thee is born, yea, unto thee—each one—is offered a knowledge, an understanding of the life of the Christ that will renew thy life, thy purpose if ye will but sing that new song, 'Love One Another.' " (262-116)

The Christmas Story

as Told by Edgar Cayce

"No Room in the Inn"

The weather was cool and there were crowds
on the way, for Bethlehem was only a
Sabbathday's journey from Jerusalem. There
were great crowds of people on the way
from the hills of Judea.

The people were active in the varied occupations of
that unusual land. Some were carpenters, as those of the
house of Joseph, who had been delayed on the journey
by the condition of the Mother. Some in this group were
helpers to Joseph—carpenters' helpers. Then there were
shepherds, husbandmen, and the varied groups from the
fields about Nazareth.

In the evening then, or at twilight, Joseph approached
the inn, which was filled with those who had also jour-
neyed there on their way to be polled for the tax imposed
by the Romans upon the people of the land. For repre-
sentatives had been sent out before time to judge the
abilities of various groups to be taxed. Each individual
was required by the Roman law to be present in the city

of his or her birth for this polling. Both Joseph and Mary were members of the religious sect called the Essenes; and thus they were to be questioned and polled by those not only in political but in religious authority in the city.

Then there was the answer by the innkeeper, "No room in the inn, especially for *such* an occasion!" Laughter and jeers followed, at the sight of the older man with the beautiful girl, his wife, who was heavy with child.

The arrival of Mary and Joseph was in the evening—not as counted by Roman time, nor by that declared to Moses by God, nor by the time which was in common usage in that land, but what would now represent January sixth.

But the story of this wondrous event at the inn actually began years before.

The purposes for which the journey was made are well known. The activities of Joseph are well known, although the difference in their ages is not so often dwelt upon. Neither is there much indicated in history as to the preparation of the Mother to be that channel through which an Immaculate Conception might take place. And this is a stumbling stone to many of the worldly-wise!

Because of the divisions that had arisen among the peoples into sects, as the Pharisee, the Sadducee, and their divisions, there had arisen the Essenes that had kept the records when individuals had experienced the supernatural or out-of-the-ordinary experiences; whether in dreams, visions, or voices that had been felt by their students throughout the experiences of this peculiar people.

There were reasons why the Essenes proclaimed that

certain periods formed cycles—reasons which grew out of their studies of Arestole, Enos, Mathias, Judah, and others who supervised the school. The Essenes were students of astrology, numerology, phrenology, and the study of the return of individuals, or reincarnation.

These Essene men and women practiced their simple faith in private, but had been persecuted by leaders of the people. This had caused the saying, as given by the Sadducees, "There is no resurrection" or "There is no reincarnation"—which is what the statement meant in that period.

In the lead of their understanding of cycles were those changes from the position of the stars that stand at the dividing of the ways between the universal vision of the solar system and those from outside the spheres. The North Star in its variation made for those cycles, and this began the Essenes' preparation for the Messiah, which took three hundred years.

Then in these signs did they see the new cycle, which was the beginning of the Piscean Age. These, then, were the beginnings. Then there was the prophecy of old which had been handed down from the experiences of the sages that an angel was to speak. When this occurred, at the choosing of the maiden who (as known only by those close to her) had been immaculately conceived, brought the preparation of a mother for the Messiah into focus.

The Maiden Mary

he Essenes maintained a purity of teaching that they hoped would fulfill the promises that had been given from the beginnings of human history—that a Messiah would come for the salvation and resurrection of the human race.

Hence there was a continued preparation and dedication of those among the Essene community who might be the channels through which this chosen vessel might enter—through choice—into materiality.

Thus in Mt. Carmel, where there were the priests of His faith, the maidens were chosen who were dedicated to this purpose, this office, this service. Among them was Mary, the beloved, the chosen one; and she, as had been foretold, was chosen as the channel. Thus she was separated and kept in closer associations with and in the care of this office.

That was the beginning. That was the foundation of what you term the Church.

For this purpose, Mary's mother, Anna, brought her to the temple when she was four years old to dedicate her in service to the studies and purposes of the Essenes. Though some doubted Anna's claim that Mary had been conceived without Anna's knowing a man, Mary had been perfect in body and in mind for service there, and she was accepted.

The students at Mt. Carmel were trained as to physical exercise, first; trained as to mental exercises as related to chastity, purity, love, patience, endurance. All of these would be termed in the present as persecutions, but they were actually tests for physical and m e n t a l s t r e n g t h , given under the supervision of those who also cared for their nourishment.

In the diet, they drank no wine, no fermented drink ever given. Special foods, yes. These were the manners and the way they were trained, directed, protected.

Mary had been studying at the school for eight years, when something wonderful happened.

"As If in Purple and Gold"

he sun shone upon the steps that led to the altar—called the temple steps—when during the first period of the morning the maidens were going to the altar for prayer, as well as to burn incense.

On this day, as they mounted the steps, all were bathed in the morning sun—which not only made a beautiful picture but clothed them all as if in purple and gold.

The elders and teachers watched the girls that morning. Mathias and Enos were there, as was Judy, the recorder and teacher who would one day teach Jesus.

Soon the girls appeared and began to climb the steps to the altar. Mary led the procession. Now nearing her thirteenth birthday, she was becoming a lovely young woman with chestnut hair and blue eyes that danced with merriment. Behind her came her friend Josie, who had become like a sister to Mary; and next, Jenife, a year younger than Mary. Jenife's gray eyes were watching Mary's bright hair as though following a beacon that day.

Then there were the others, Andra, Sophia, and the other Mary, many of whom remained friends with Mary and Jesus all their lives.

Farther back in the line, Edithia walked with her dark head bent, deep in thought and prayer. Edithia and Jenife were sisters, the daughters of an innkeeper who kept an inn near Bethlehem.

As Mary reached the top step there was thunder and lightning. She stood still, her eyes looking up in radiant wonder and awe. A great halo of light formed around her, and within the light, the angel Gabriel appeared, taking the child by the hand before the altar. Wide-eyed, Judy stood still. Mathias drew in his breath sharply, and Enos stifled a cry. This was the manner of choice; this was the showing of the way, for Mary had led the others on *this* day!

After a moment, the vision ended, and Judy directed the girls to take their usual places. Josie and Jenife were stunned by what had happened to Mary.

It would be three more years before Mary would conceive the Christ-Child, and longer still before she would join Joseph. But as that time approached, the famed Wise Men had already begun their journey, and Mary's teacher, Judy, had begun to play a role in what would now unfold in the land.

Mary at Sixteen

nce their schooling was complete, about three years after the appearance of the angel Gabriel to Mary on the stair, all of the students at Mt. Carmel returned to their homes.

At sixteen, Mary had become a beautiful young woman. She was serene and happy by nature.

One day, when she was alone in her favorite meditation place, the angel Gabriel again suddenly appeared beside her.

"Hail!" he greeted her. "You who are highly favored. The Lord is with you. Blessed are you among women!"

Mary was troubled at his saying, but the angel said, "Fear not, Mary, for you have found favor with God. And behold, you shall conceive in your womb and bring forth a son."

Startled, Mary could only ask, "How can these things be?"

Gabriel answered, "You will be overshadowed by the

Holy Spirit and conceive a child," he explained. "His name shall be Jesus, and He will be known as the Son of God."

He also told her that her cousin, Elizabeth, whom many thought was too old to have children, was now expecting a son.

Awed by the experience, Mary whispered, "Behold the handmaiden of the Lord. Be it unto me according to your word."

Within a few weeks, Mary discovered that she was with child.

Mary's
Immaculate Conception

any people believe that Mary conceived her child, Jesus, without knowing man, but few understand how this was possible. Fewer still, however, know that Mary's mother, Anna, had also conceived Mary through an Immaculate Conception.

Anna had only been informed generally that she would conceive her child in this way—not the way Mary was informed—and when she proclaimed this fact, no one believed her, saying that it wasn't in compliance with natural law.

In special cases, such as Anna's and Mary's, for the purpose of bringing the divine plan to earth, these spiritual conceptions *were* natural. Natural, as is demonstrated by the very projection of mind into matter, thus making of itself a separation encased in matter, as humankind has done in itself.

As flesh is the activity of the spiritual self and mental being pushing itself into matter; and as spirit, as He gave, is neither male nor female, they are then both, or one. And when humanity had reached that period when there was full separation from God, then flesh as men and women know it today became a reality in the material plane.

So, the Immaculate Conception means that the physical and mental are so attuned to spirit as to be quickened by it.

Hence the spirit, the soul of the Master, then, was brought into being, through the accord of the Mother in materiality, by what you know in the earth plane as conception.

Joseph's Courage

ike Mary, Joseph was of the lineage of the house of David. He was thirty-six when he was first told about the role he would play. He had been first informed about the coming birth of Jesus by Mathias and Judah at Mt. Carmel, around the time when Mary was chosen by Archangel Gabriel on the stair.

The pair was matched as in a lodge, not as you would term by visitations; neither as only chosen by the sect or the families. In those periods in most of the Jewish families the arrangements were made by the parents, you see; while in this case these two were not as contracting parties from their families. For Anna and her daughter were questioned as belonging to any family!

But when Joseph first learned the news, he was disturbed because of how much older he was than Mary. He was especially disturbed about what people would say!

During the three to four years before Mary became with child, while she was still in training, Joseph received guidance—first in a dream and then by direct voice. Whenever there is the voice in such guidance, there are also fragrances and visions.

Once he was assured that his role was divine will, he knew that he would fulfill it. When he went to claim her for his bride, a girl of sixteen, she was already with child.

They were married in the temple, there at Mt. Carmel, when Joseph was thirty-six and Mary was sixteen. During her pregnancy, Mary would spend most of her time in the hills of Judea, and only a portion of the time with Joseph in Nazareth.

Mary Visits Elizabeth

hen Mary went to the hill country, she visited her cousin, Elizabeth, who was much older. Once Elizabeth saw Mary, she realized that Mary's baby would become the Messiah and that her own expected child would help prepare people to receive Him.

"I am honored to have the Mother of my Lord in my house!" she told Mary.

"My soul magnifies the Lord!" Mary said. "He has done to me great things, and henceforth, all generations shall call me blessed!"

Happily the older woman and her young cousin passed the peaceful days preparing for the arrival of their babies. They were attended to by a midwife named Margil, who also counseled them during their pregnancies. Anna, the aged seeress, who would be termed the "waiting maid" when they were each heavy with child, was also there. Anna was the seeress who blessed them both and made those prophecies as to what would be the material experience of each in the earth.

Mary had been visited many times by the angel. In the temple when she was chosen, in the home of Elizabeth when she was made aware of the presence, and by being again in the presence of the messenger or forerunner, who was John. The angel also visited Joseph at the time of their union. Again (by Michael) at the time when the edict was given.

After Elizabeth's son, John, was born, and as the time drew near for the birth of her baby, Mary joined Joseph in Nazareth. From there, Joseph and Mary went to Bethlehem to be taxed, or to register, as you would term it.

A Babe in the Stable

t had been difficult enough for Joseph, being ordered by law to take Mary, nearly ready to give birth, on the journey to Bethlehem. But his troubles increased when the innkeeper, Apsaphar, told him that there was no room at the inn.

Disappointment was written upon the face of Joseph, and also on the face of the innkeeper's daughters, as well as those of certain groups about the inn, for many saw the possibilities of an unusual story if the birth were to take place there. Also there was consternation outside, among those Essenes who had heard that Joseph and Mary had arrived and were not given a room. They began to seek some place, some shelter.

This was no ordinary inn, for remember, many of those present were also of that questioned group, the Essenes. They had heard of the girl, that lovely wife of Joseph who had been chosen by the angel on the stair. They had heard of what had taken place in the hills where Eliza-

beth had gone, when she was visited by this girl, her cousin. Such stories were whispered from one to another.

Thus many joined in the search for some place to let them stay. Necessity demanded that some place be sought—quickly. Then it was found, a cleft or grotto, under the hill, in the stable, above which the shepherds were gathering their flocks into the fold.

As it happened, Apsaphar was the father of two of Mary's fellow students at Mt. Carmel—Edithia and Jenife. So when Apsaphar made the joke about there being no room, he did this rather for protection than because—as has been said—there was "no room in the inn." But this was meant to be implied or conveyed that they were "turned away." For Apsaphar, also of the Essenes, had also seen a vision; Apsaphar, too, had heard, had known of the voices that were in the air. He, too, had seen the star in the East. He, too, had known of those experiences that must befall those who were making all the preparations possible under those existent conditions for Him that should come as a teacher, as a shepherd, as a Savior.

Apsaphar had another daughter named Sarapha, who was just a year younger than the little Mother. Sarapha had known of the preparations through the Essene meetings that were forbidden by Jewish and Roman law. It was she who helped prepare those quarters to which the Mother-to-be and the father might come.

Then when it was known to Sarapha that the stable had been occupied—oh, the rush; oh, the desire to be off to see what that experience might be, held her very being!

As soon as her duties were cleared about the home—as

the space was very near—Sarapha started. But as she walked into the open air upon that eve the brightness of His star came nearer and nearer. And Sarapha heard, even as did the shepherds, "Peace on earth. Good will to all of good faith!"—while all the rabble, all the jeers of a world were stopped!

All felt the vibrations and saw a great light—not only the shepherds above the stable but those in the inn. To be sure, those emotions were later to be dispelled by the doubters, who told the people that they had been overcome by wine or whatnot.

But just as the midnight hour came, there was the birth of the Master. Then Sarapha, daughter of the innkeeper, was soon upon the scene, as was her mother, Sodaphe; and the shepherds who had answered the cry and gone to see what had come to pass.

There, in the stable in the grotto in the hill, the Savior, the Child was born; who, through the will and the life He manifested, became the Savior of the world—that channel through which those of old had been told that the promise made to Eve would be fulfilled: the arising again of another like unto Moses. And as given to David, the promised One was not to depart from the channel of his descendants.

Lower and lower humankind's concepts had fallen. Then, when hope seemed gone, the herald angels sang. The star appeared that made wonderment to the shepherds, that caused awe and consternation to all of those about the inn. Some made fun; some were smitten with conviction that the unkind things they had said needed

to be readjusted in their relationship to things coming to pass.

All were in awe as the brightness of His star appeared and shone; as the music of the spheres brought that joyful choir, *"Peace on earth! Good will to all of good faith!"*

The Shepherds and
the Wise Men

mong the shepherds was Joel, who had been known for his poems and the songs that he often sang. Other shepherds came, too, to see the newborn Jesus. Eucuo was there, and so was Thaddeus. So was Slocombi, a relative of Elizabeth and her new baby, John, who would be the preparer of the way. All of these, and more, heard the song of the angels, "Glory to God in the highest. Peace on earth and good will to all people."

As for the Wise Men, who were they? And what were they really like?

There were people throughout the whole world who looked for and sought a better understanding of God's laws. These were students who had succeeded in subduing the materialistic urges arising from the projection of the souls into matter. These were called wise ones, or sages. They were in accord with the high purposes held by Jesus.

We find, then, that the Wise Men were those who were seekers for the truth about this event. Through the application of those forces which today you would term "psychic," we find the Wise Men coming to the place "where the Child was." Or they were drawn to give thanks for this gift, this expression of a soul seeking to show a wayward humanity the path back to God.

So the three Wise Men represent in a metaphysical sense the three phases of human experience in materiality—gold, the material; frankincense, the ether or ethereal; myrrh, the healing force; or body, mind, and soul.

These were the symbolic meanings then of the Wise Men in their relationship. Or, to put this into the parlance of the day, they were the encouragement needed for the Mother and those who had nourished, who had cherished this event in the experience of humankind. They actually came during Mary's month of purification or recovery according to Jewish law. To be sure, only after Mary was purified were they presented to the Child.

Not well known is the fact that there was more than one visit by Wise Men. One is a record of three Wise Men. But, there was the fourth, as well as the fifth, and then the second group. They came from Persia, India, Egypt, and also from Chaldea, Gobi, and what is now the Indo or Tao land.

The Part That Judy Played

n the day when Mary was chosen on the stair, Judy was twenty-one years old. She was a leader with the Brotherhood who was guiding the Essenes—though the elders had expected her to be a boy! In addition to being a teacher, she was the recorder of the spiritual experiences of the Essenes. She would also be one of Jesus' teachers after His birth—one of the ones who would send Him to Egypt and India during those mysterious eighteen years of His life that the Bible does not mention.

In her work, Judy recorded the traditions of Egypt, the traditions from India, the conditions and traditions from many of the Persian lands, and many of the borders about Persia became a part of the studies—to make, keep, and preserve such records.

Owing to the political situations that gradually arose due to the Roman influence in the land, Judy had been content and reclusive in her early years. But that all changed when she was visited by the Wise Men of the

East—one from Persia, one from India, one from the Egyptian land. Achlar was among them. And so was Ashtueil.

The Wise Men reasoned with the Essene brethren, but more was sought from Judy's studies. Then there was the report by the Wise Men to the king. Has it been thought of, or have you ever wondered why the Wise Men went to Herod, who was only second or third in authority, rather than to the Romans who were *all* authority in the land?

Because of Judy, knowing that this would arouse in the heart and mind of this debased ruler—that only sought for the aggrandizement of self—such reactions as to bring to him, this despot, turmoils with those then in authority.

Why? There was not the proclamation by the Wise Men, neither by Judy nor the Essenes, that this new king was to replace Rome! It was to replace the Jewish authority in the land!

Thus we find, as it would be termed in the present, attention was called to the activity of the Essenes such that a little later—during those periods of the sojourn of the Child in Egypt because of him—Herod issued the edict for the destruction of all the newborn sons in Judea.

Josie and the Sojourn in Egypt

hen, when there was the fulfilling of those periods when Mary was espoused to Joseph and was to give birth to the Savior, the Messiah, the Prince of Peace, the Way, the Truth, the Light—soon after this birth there was the issuing of the orders first by Judy that there should be someone selected to be with the parents during their period of sojourn in Egypt. This was owing to the conditions which arose from the visit of the Wise Men and their not returning to Herod to report, when the decrees were issued that there should be the destruction of the children of that age from six months to two years, especially in that region from Bethany to Nazareth.

After Jesus' birth, there was a period of purification according to the law, then the days in the temple and the blessing by Anna and by the high priest. And these constituted the early days of the beginning of the entity called Jesus, who becomes the Christ, the Master of masters. During this period there was the return to Nazareth and

then the edict that sent them into Egypt so that the prophecy might be fulfilled, *"My son shall be called from Egypt."*

Josie, Mary's childhood friend from Mt. Carmel, had been very close to the activities of the innkeeper who made the preparation—owing to the closeness of the family to which she then joined, from the activities of the Essenes and the holy ones, for the protection of the individual activity.

Josie chose to join with the holy family and acted in the capacity of the handmaid to the Mother, the Child, and waited on Joseph during those sojourns; dwelling by the brooks or the places where there were wells, in the upper portion of the Egyptian land to which they fled.

Thus, this entity, Josie, was selected or chosen by those of the Brotherhood—sometimes called the White Brotherhood in the present—as the handmaid or companion of Mary, Jesus, and Joseph, in their flight into Egypt.

During those periods of the journey Josie ministered; and it was no mean distance for a very young Child and a very young Mother—during such delicate conditions.

This began on an evening, and the journey—through portions of Palestine, from Nazareth to the borders of Egypt—was made only during the night.

Do not understand that there was only Joseph, Mary, Josie, and the Child. For there were other groups that preceded and followed; that there might be the physical protection of the fulfilling of the Promised One.

In the journeys to Egypt, little of great significance might be indicated, but the care and attention to the

Child and the Mother was greatly in Josie's hands through that journey.

The period of sojourn in Egypt was in and about what was then Alexandria. Josie and Mary were not idle during that sojourn, but part of what they did there was preserved in the records of the libraries there. The interest in those records was reported to the Brotherhood in the Judean country.

The sojourn there was a period of some four years—four years, six months, three days. Then there was the return to Judea and to Capernaum, where dwelt many of those who later were the closer companions of the Master.

But the entity Josie, following the return, was active in all educational activities as well as in the care of the body and attending to those things pertaining to household duties with every child. And Josie was among those who went with Mary and Joseph when they went to the city, Jerusalem, at the time of His age of twelve. It was thought by Joseph and Mary that He had stayed in the care of Josie when He was missed; when there was the returning to find Him in the temple.

After the period of presentation at the temple, when there were certain questionings among groups of the leaders, Jesus was sent first—again—into Egypt for only a short period, and then into India, and then into what is now Persia.

Hence Jesus was trained in all the ways of the various teachers.

From Persia he was called to Judea at the death of Joseph, and then into Egypt for the completion of His preparation as a teacher. He was with John, the messenger, during a portion of His training there in Egypt.

Then he returned to Capernaum, Cana, and there came the periods of first preparation, in the land of His nativity.

The rest ye have according to Mark, John, Matthew, and Luke; these in their order record most of the material experiences of the Master.

More About Christmas

A Christmas Message

(On December 12, 1936, members of the Norfolk, Virginia, A.R.E. Study Group No. 1, compilers of the book, *A Search for God*, requested a reading from Edgar Cayce which would give them a better understanding and a deeper appreciation of the birth of Jesus, the Christ. This reading, 262-103, was given.)

YES, WE HAVE THE GROUP GATHERED HERE; their desires, their seeking, as a group and as individuals.

To these, then, who seek to know more of that circumstance and of those conditions which surrounded what you call the first Christmas, we would give: Do not confuse yourselves. While to you it may seem to be the first Christmas, if it were the first then there would be a last, and you would not worship nor hold to that which passes.

Time never was when there was not a Christ and not a Christ-mass.

But in giving that interpretation of what this season means—the birth of Jesus who became the Christ—to this world: Much has been recorded respecting the circumstance by the writers of the gospel, especially by Luke; but no perfect concept may be gathered except by you as individuals seeking to experience what such an advent meant, or means, to your life as an individual.

For the knowledge of a happening or condition, and

42

the wisdom which is presented by that happening, are two different things. What you hear you may believe, but you will rarely act as if you believed it unless you have experienced, and do experience, that God so loved the world as to give His Son to enter into flesh, in order that flesh, humanity, might know there is an advocate with the Father. In your material experience you see that life came out of nowhere to enter into materiality, to become a living expression of those promptings of the heart. It has been the experience of that Christ *Soul* in its own varied spheres of consciousness to give you such an expression. That is the purpose for which He has entered—to give us a more perfect concept of the relationship between ourselves and our Creator.

Thus we find that event in Bethlehem of Judea ages ago, when Mary, that channel, had so dedicated herself to the service of her Maker as to become Mother. Therein the whole world is shown that this must come to pass in the experience of those who would make themselves channels through which the Holy Spirit of God may manifest. Thus the world may know that He, God the Father, keeps His promises with the children of men and women!

Then the hour approached when nature was to be fulfilled in the natural course in the experience of the Mother, and His star appeared, and the angels' choir, and the voices of those who gave the *Great Message!*

Who Heard the Angels Sing?

WHO HEARD THESE, MY CHILDREN? Those who were seeking for the satisfying of their own desires, or for the laudation of their own personality? Rather those close to *nature*, to the hours of meditation and prayer; and those who had given expression, "No room in the inn!" For no inn, no room, could contain that which was being given in a manifested form!

He came unto His own. For there was nothing made to which He had not given life, to whom He had not given "Be ye fruitful, multiply" in thyself. In thyself may there be the propagation of thine own species, of thine own self!

Only, then, to those who sought could such a message come, or could there be heard the songs of the angels, or that music of the spheres which sang, *"Peace on earth! Good will to all!"*

For this, then, *is* in every birth—the possibilities, the glories, the reactivating of the influence of that entrance of God-man into the earth, in order that we might know the way.

It comes at this time to bring to your hearts and minds the gladness of that period and the fact that not only 1,900 years ago but today, He may be born into our own consciousness, our own understanding. He comes unto His own!

Are we His? Have we claimed Him? Have we put on the Christ, even as exemplified in the life, the birth, the death of Jesus, the Christ?

He is our Elder Brother. He is the Babe in our hearts, in our lives, to be nourished now, even as then, in our hearts, in our bodies, in our minds.

Then indeed do His words become more and more meaningful, "As ye do it unto the least of these, thy brethren, ye do it unto me!"

So May We Hasten the Day

FOR AS WE BEHOLD the face of our friend, of our neighbor, of our foe—yes, our enemy—we behold the image of our Savior. For we are all His, bought not only by birth of the God-Child into flesh but by the death; so that we might know that He, our Brother, our Savior, our Christ, has been the Way, and is the Way, to the Father in this material plane.

Just as He chose to enter, so we have entered. Because He chose to live, we may live. As He chose to give of Himself in order that there might be a greater understanding, a greater knowledge—may we give of ourselves.

As changes come and we show forth the raising of that consciousness of His presence in our experience, by our dealings and conversations and by our very lives with and among our fellow human beings; so may we hasten the day when He, the Christ, may come into our own hearts, unto His own people, to reign, yes, in our hearts and lives!

"That Ye Love One Another"

IN CONSIDERING CONDITIONS that exist in the world, it is well that those present think how they themselves may be the means by which they may induce others to consider the purpose of Christmas—the purpose for which the Christ came into the earth:

First, that the level of our consciousness might become such that we, humanity, could be as much aware of God as of ourselves.

Second, as given in each of His promises to us, that love might abound; there might be a continuous communion with God through the Son, who offered Himself as a means for our approach to the Father.

So, this message to all:

Keep that awareness of His presence. As He has given, "Lo, I am with you always, even unto the end of the world." And though there may be abroad hate, avarice, selfishness, and conditions which make us afraid; be still within thine own heart, thine own consciousness, and know that He is with thee.

As ye give, so will ye receive. As He hath spoken, love of the Father to the children of men and women is manifested in the spirit of Christmas—a Christ-mass—that which may now because of Him be raised to that consciousness, that level above humanity's way of thought, humanity's concept of force, power, or might; and that the real strength, the real hope, the real contribution is in the still, small voice within.

Not in the tempest, not in the roar, nor the lore of the might of battle; though there may be the destruction of life, of property (as is known materially), no one can destroy the soul but self! No one but self!

God hath not willed that any soul should perish, but hath given even His Son, who brought into the world the spirit of Christmas.

Let thy message be: There is hope in Him. For He has given the promise, "Lo, I am with thee always, even unto the end of the world."

And though the world, the earth may pass away; though it may be burned up; though it may bring destruction to the material things; we look to Him and we know there is safety in Him.

Fear not the one who may destroy the body, but rather fear one who may destroy the soul in torment. In love, then, in obedience, in prayer, follow Him.

Let that heart, that mind then be in thee which was in Him—"that ye love one another."

How to Celebrate Christmas

THEN INDEED SHOULD EACH OF US at the Glad Season make the hearts of others merry by our own happiness in the birth, the life, the death of our Jesus, our Christ!

Let us realize that this had no beginning in the 1,900 years ago, but again and again and again! And it may be today—He may be born into our consciousness; not as a physical birth, but each moment when a physical birth is experienced in the earth, there is an opportunity for the Christ entrance again!

What, then, are we doing about it in our daily lives, in our daily conversations?

For it is not by might nor in power, but in the still, small voice speaking from within, that we may know. As He has so oft given, "Peace! It is I! Be not afraid, it is *I!*"— thy Savior, thy Christ. Yes, we ourselves are meeting that *Babe*: in our own inner selves, in order that we may grow, even as He, to be a channel of blessings to others!

Then as we do it unto others we do it unto Him.

May the peace, the joy of His consciousness, His presence, His joy be yours this day—yes, all your days in the earth. For He is nigh unto you; He is in your midst!

Then let us praise the Lord who gave His Son in order that we might know Him!

Readings List

The following is a list of the Edgar Cayce readings from which material has been drawn for the preparation of this book:

Achlar	1908-1
Apsaphar, the innkeeper	1196-2, 5749-13
Ashtueil	256-1
A Christmas Message	262-103
The Christmas Spirit Within	262-116
Edithia	587-3
Essenes	5749-13
Eucuo	1815-1
How to Celebrate Christmas	262-103
Jenife and Serapha	1152-1
Joel	1859-1
Josie	1010-12, -17, 5749-7
Judy and the Essenes	1472-1, -3
Main Story	5749-8
Mary	1222-1, 1648-1, 5749-7
A Psalm for Christmas	281-14
Slocombi	519-1
So We May Hasten the Day	262-103
Thaddeus	2562-1
"That Ye Love One Another"	281-59
Who Heard the Angels Sing?	262-103
Wise Men	2067-7, 5749-7

About the Illustrator

Glenna Hartwell received her training at The Cape School of Art, in Provincetown, Massachusetts. She worked for many years as a portrait artist before she began her career in illustration. Her work has appeared in numerous calendars, magazines, and on greeting cards.

EDGAR CAYCE

Edgar Cayce was born in Kentucky in 1877.

When he was thirteen years old, he had a vision of an angel while he was reading alone in the woods near his home. The angel asked him what he would like most of all in his life. He replied, "I would like to be helpful to others, especially to children when they are sick."

As he grew up, Edgar Cayce discovered he had a rare gift. That gift was information that came to him in a special way and allowed him to help sick children and grown-ups get well. His gift also enabled him to help a lot of people solve many different kinds of problems.

Edgar Cayce died in 1945.

Today he is known as a person who spent his life helping others through his special gift, which is called "psychic ability."

What Is A.R.E.?

The Association for Research and Enlightenment, Inc. (A.R.E.®), is the international headquarters for the work of Edgar Cayce (1877-1945), who is considered the best-documented psychic of the twentieth century. Founded in 1931, the A.R.E. consists of a community of people from all walks of life and spiritual traditions, who have found meaningful and life-transformative insights from the readings of Edgar Cayce.

Although A.R.E. headquarters is located in Virginia Beach, Virginia—where visitors are always welcome—the A.R.E. community is a global network of individuals who offer conferences, educational activities, and fellowship around the world. People of every age are invited to participate in programs that focus on such topics as holistic health, dreams, reincarnation, ESP, the power of the mind, meditation, and personal spirituality.

In addition to study groups and various activities, the A.R.E. offers membership benefits and services, a bimonthly magazine, a newsletter, extracts from the Cayce readings, conferences, international tours, a massage school curriculum, an impressive volunteer network, a retreat-type camp for children and adults, and A.R.E. contacts around the world. A.R.E. also maintains an affiliation with Atlantic University, which offers a master's degree program in Transpersonal Studies.

For additional information about A.R.E. activities hosted near you, please contact:

A.R.E.
67th St. and Atlantic Ave.
P.O. Box 595
Virginia Beach, VA 23451-0595
(757) 428-3588

A.R.E. Press

A.R.E. Press is a publisher and distributor of books, audiotapes, and videos that offer guidance for a more fulfilling life. Our products are based on, or are compatible with, the concepts in the psychic readings of Edgar Cayce.

For a free catalog, please write to A.R.E. Press at the address below or call toll free 1-800-723-1112. For any other information, please call 757-428-3588.

A.R.E. Press
Sixty-Eighth & Atlantic Avenue
P.O. Box 656
Virginia Beach, VA 23451-0656